RETURN OF THE PADAWAN

by *New York Times* bestselling author
Jeffrey Brown

Scholastic Inc.

Thanks to everyone who helped make this book not only possible, but better: Rex, Sam, Rick, and everyone at Scholastic; Joanne, Leland, Carol, J.W. Rinzler, and everyone at Lucasfilm; Marc Gerald, Chris Staros, Brett Warnock, Steve Mockus, my readers, friends, and family – especially Jennifer, Oscar, and Simon. Thank you!

www.starwars.com
www.scholastic.com

Library of Congress Control Number 2014931163

ISBN 978-0-545-77317-1

10 9 8 7 6 5 4 3   14 15 16 17 18 19/0

Printed in the U.S.A.   23
This edition first printing, September 2014

A long time ago in a galaxy far, far away....

There was a boy named Roan Novachez (that's me) who ALWAYS wanted to be a pilot but ended up at JEDI ACADEMY. His first year started off REALLY BAD but ended up great! This school year will definitely be the BEST YEAR EVER!

me when I first got to Jedi Academy

me, when I start Year Two: Jedi pilot training!

8

WELCOME BACK TO JEDI ACADEMY

As students return to Coruscant for another year at Jedi Academy, they can expect to continue the best Jedi training in the galaxy, under the instruction of an experienced Jedi staff, including Master Yoda. This year, students will enter an exciting new phase of their training, as they learn to pilot Jedi starfighters in state-of-the-art flight simulators, continue learning to use the Force, and resist the dark side.

MEET OUR NEWEST STAFF MEMBER, GAMMY! Our new cafeteria chef, Gammy, is the first Gamorrean to achieve the rank of galactic gourmet after spending years training at some of the best restaurants on the planet Lamaredd. He will be introducing a number of delicious new meals to the cafeteria, including traditional Gamorrean mushroom, liver, and eyeball recipes.

THIS YEAR, our Padawan will enjoy the opportunity to care for a class pet, this voorpak from Naboo. Students will make sure the voorpak's soft fur stays clean and feed the voorpak its diet of live insects.

TRIDAY

I can tell Mom is really going to miss me this school year because she's been very huggy this summer whenever I've been at home. The best thing this summer was definitely going on the Corellian Run with Dad and Pasha. Dad showed us some tricks and even let us help with the ~~maintenance~~ maintenance checks on his starship. Dav was taking summer classes so I didn't see him as much, but we holochatted a bunch. I tried to holochat with Gaiana but kept missing her. She went on a family vacation to Naboo. She sent me a colo claw fish tooth, which is pretty cool. I drew a picture of a colo to send back to her. It'll be really good to see her and Pasha back at school, especially since we'll get to flight train. Finally, a class about something I'm good at! The only downside is the food at Jedi Academy....The cafeteria food ended up being edible, but it's not nearly as good as Mom's food. And Mom never makes me eat ANYTHING that stares at me before I eat it!

Awww, sweetie!

MONODAY

I can't believe how boring Jedi Academy is. Nobody else is here yet. It turns out I got here a couple days early. I guess I was too excited and didn't look at the calendar right. Fortunately, Master Yoda has been around, getting ready for class. At least, I think he's getting

I was finally the first one to class!

Saved seats for Pasha and Gaiana

ready for class... he's just shuffling around, going through stuff in cupboards and taking things out. He

Mmmh heh heh!

started me on some new exercises using the Force, so I've been getting back into

the swing of things. Everyone else should start showing up tomorrow. I'm so ready for school to finally begin!

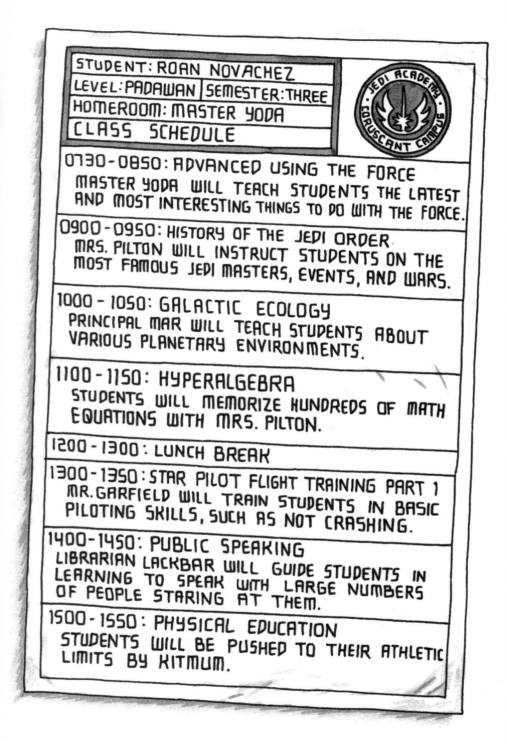

STUDENT: ROAN NOVACHEZ
LEVEL: PADAWAN | SEMESTER: THREE
HOMEROOM: MASTER YODA

CLASS SCHEDULE

0730-0850: ADVANCED USING THE FORCE
MASTER YODA WILL TEACH STUDENTS THE LATEST AND MOST INTERESTING THINGS TO DO WITH THE FORCE.

0900-0950: HISTORY OF THE JEDI ORDER
MRS. PILTON WILL INSTRUCT STUDENTS ON THE MOST FAMOUS JEDI MASTERS, EVENTS, AND WARS.

1000-1050: GALACTIC ECOLOGY
PRINCIPAL MAR WILL TEACH STUDENTS ABOUT VARIOUS PLANETARY ENVIRONMENTS.

1100-1150: HYPERALGEBRA
STUDENTS WILL MEMORIZE HUNDREDS OF MATH EQUATIONS WITH MRS. PILTON.

1200-1300: LUNCH BREAK

1300-1350: STAR PILOT FLIGHT TRAINING PART 1
MR. GARFIELD WILL TRAIN STUDENTS IN BASIC PILOTING SKILLS, SUCH AS NOT CRASHING.

1400-1450: PUBLIC SPEAKING
LIBRARIAN LACKBAR WILL GUIDE STUDENTS IN LEARNING TO SPEAK WITH LARGE NUMBERS OF PEOPLE STARING AT THEM.

1500-1550: PHYSICAL EDUCATION
STUDENTS WILL BE PUSHED TO THEIR ATHLETIC LIMITS BY KITMUM.

It's been good to finally catch up with Gaiana and Pasha this week. I think not hanging out with them so much was really what made the summer seem like it was a super-long time. I've been looking forward to pilot training ~~all summer~~ <u>my entire life</u> and now that we're starting training, I find out I still have to wait to do any flying!

me, waiting ← waiting waiting waiting

The only thing we're doing for the first couple weeks is reading through the Galactic Pilot General Instruction Flight Training Manual and Workbook, which weighs more than our class pet, Voorpee. In fact, it probably weighs more than Egon!

↑ Normal textbook

GALACTIC PILOT GENERAL INSTRUCTION FLIGHT TRAINING MANUAL AND WORKBOOK

9th ed.

G.P.G.I.F.T.M.A.W.

Egon holding the manual

Mr. Garfield says we HAVE to learn EVERYTHING in the book backward and forward before we even step into a flight simulator. That's RIDICULOUS. Reading a book can't

THIS IS IMPORTANT!

(Mr. G. thinks EVERYTHING he says is important.)

give you the feeling of what flying is like! I think you can't understand something unless you really ~~experiense~~ experience it. It's not like flight simulators can put us in any actual danger. At least this isn't a super-boring or super-hard class for me, or I'd be even more frustrated. Of course, I have to spend so much time reading the G.P.G.I.F.T.M.A.W. that I haven't come up with any ideas to draw for Ewok Pilot comics for the school paper. A couple people have ~~alreddy~~ already asked if I've drawn any new ones, so I'll try to come up with ideas soon...

Hey, Ewok Pilot, here's the updated flight manual.

I think it'll be really useful to you!

sniff sniff

Bugdoo!

The Padawan Observer

EDITED BY THE STUDENTS OF JEDI ACADEMY· VOL. MXIII #1

WELCOME BACK!

The Padawans of the Coruscant Jedi Academy returned for an exciting first week. Students were reportedly extremely excited for star pilot training, as shown by instructor Mr. Garfield's request for additional air sickness bags. Master Yoda was pleased with his first class, except that "lifting things with the Force all the time, too many students were." Meanwhile, Librarian

Lackbar announced the first student social activity. "It's a dance!" she said. "It will be a Satine Hawkins dance, where girls ask boys." Padawans are asked to avoid wearing extra robes, which can be dangerous if the dancing is overly energetic.

Everyone here is really into Holobook but I'm starting to think the only thing it's used for is making fun of me. I also don't know how anyone has time to update so much, with all of the homework we have. I thought I might save some time by signing up for tutoring sessions with T-P30, but I found out he actually makes

...in fact, your algebra problem reminds me of how traditional Mandalorian poetry is often such a part of culture that the lack of verb voice blah blah blah...

doing homework take LONGER. I think the teachers are giving us more homework this year, too. Maybe that's why they're giving us a school dance so early in the semester? It'll be good because I'll have a chance to spend time with Gaiana. We hung out a little last week, I guess, but it would be cool to see her at the dance. We could even hang out afterward, if she's not doing anything else.

QUADDAY

After the dance, Gaiana asked to switch seats from next to me in homeroom. She must be mad at me, but I didn't do anything. The dodgeball thing was an accident. I hope she wasn't changing seats because of me. Maybe it was because of Cronah, who's been shooting spitballs at me, but his aim isn't great and sometimes they hit her. Pasha sits on the other side of me, but he learned how to use the Force to deflect the spitballs.

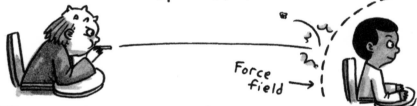

Force field →

The good news is that tomorrow we're FINALLY going to get to use the star pilot simulators in flight training class! Finally, something I'VE been preparing my whole life for. After this, no one will look at me the same, because I'm going to beat all of their test scores by a whole bunch. I'll show them!!

Star pilot training has so far **NOT** been going according to plan. It turns out reading the G.P.G.I.F.T.M.A.W. is important, because Mr. Garfield makes us take a quiz on it every other day. I bet he has to spend all night thinking of questions for them. Then there was the ~~incidint~~ incident with the flight simulator, which totally CAN'T be my fault. Everyone was looking at me like

Seat **not** cushiony!

crack in view screen

loose cable

dusty, uncleaned vent

I was a doofus, but that thing was already old and falling apart. No one will believe me because now it's even more broken down. When we get to use the simulators again, everyone will expect me to be perfect, or they'll give me a super-hard time. I'm going to have to work harder than anyone, which isn't fair.

Ewok Pilot, do you know what this part is for?

Danthee?

Gammy's
MENU

Entrees
- Nuggets (I don't know what they're made of either) served with SARLACC MUCUS dipping sauce
- Mystery salad (similar to "surprise salad"), topped with Cularin slug skin flakes
- Mushrooms (mixed in bowl with other stuff I have lying around on the floor)

Sides
- Mook fruit (served ice cold)
- Vegetable soup (served boiling hot)
- Spicy "stuff" (includes medical burn kit)
* we are out of fruits and vegetables

Drinks
- Water
- Brownish/greenish water (probably safe)
- Fizzy water (womp-rat tail flavored)

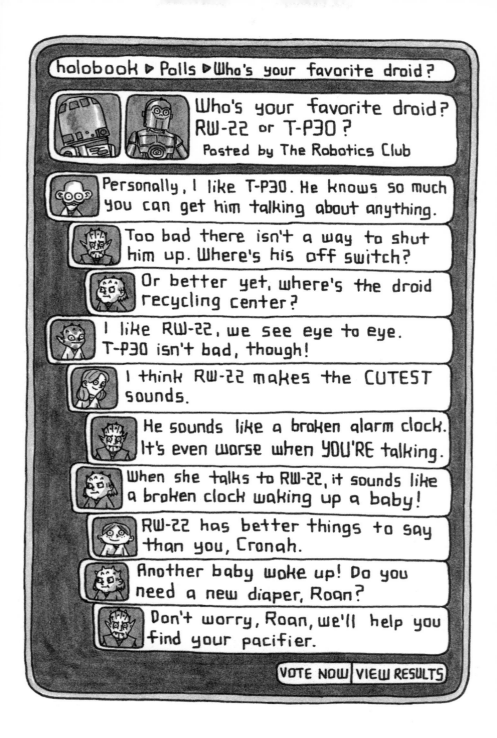

DUODAY

It turns out we're getting new star pilot simulators. We were already scheduled to get them, so the simulator that exploded when I was in it must have already been old and broken. No one seems to think that, though. I don't know how just pushing a bunch of buttons could break it! I've been re-reading the G.P.G.I.F.T.M.A.W.

Save yourself, RW-22, everything Roan touches EXPLODES!

BLOOP?

and I'm sure I entered all of the codes in the right sequence. Well, pretty sure. I'm going to keep studying until I can show everyone that I really know what I'm doing. I'm also starting work on my project for Librarian Lackbar's public speaking class. We all have a solo project where we stand up and give a "how-to" speech in front of the class. Which kind of sounds like the teachers getting us to do their work for them, even if Librarian Lackbar says it's so that we'll learn about speaking in public (which Jedi have to do as peacekeepers) and working alone (which is how Jedi have to work sometimes). It's funny that Librarian Lackbar is teaching this class, because she sounds like she's talking underwater. I think I've got a good idea for my presentation. I'm going to give a speech about ~~medatating~~ meditating. I'm going to make it funny and entertaining, everyone will enjoy that. Maybe I'll even make a minicomic

Meditating, guys, am I right?

to hand out with my talk. I could also check out the Jedi Archives. There's some great books I could find with information that Master Yoda hasn't taught us yet. The neat thing is that if everyone falls asleep during my speech, it means I gave a good speech, not a boring one!

You must unlearn what you have learned.

Then learn it again, you must!

45

Hey Ro-

Sorry to hear about the star pilot simulator blowing up, but I can laugh about it WITH you, right? Seriously, though, don't worry about it. Old technology is always breaking down.
I wouldn't think too much about not dancing with Gaiana, either. It doesn't mean she doesn't like you. Just make sure you listen to her, be patient, and be nice to her. Don't get all pushy! Trust me, this is good advice — my girlfriend, Enowyn, gave it to me, and she hasn't dumped me yet...

                              -Dav

P.S. Send more comics, I need more stuff to read here!

Things Yoda Said This Week

Adventure. Heh. Excitement. Heh. A Jedi craves not these things.

The good from bad, a Jedi knows when he is calm, at peace. Passive.

calm

at peace

(maybe Yoda is wrinkly from spending lots of time relaxing in hot baths!)

You must feel the Force around you; here, between you, me, the tree, the rock, everywhere.

Even between your desk and your homework.

Yesterday, I caught Ronald looking at my quiz paper AGAIN. He gets okay grades, so I bet he cheats all the time. At first I wondered why he would need to cheat if he's getting okay grades, but now I think it's WHY he gets okay grades. It's weird that our class student council president isn't a better student. Or maybe not focusing on his classes is what makes him a good president? I don't know, but it's REALLY ANNOYING. I should probably say something and get him in trouble, but then everyone will think I'M the jerk, when he's the jerk. For my solo presentation, I finished putting together my minicomic handout. Bill, Egon, and Pasha helped me put them together.

cut copies in half | put pages in order | Fold | Staple

HOW TO MEDITATE USING THE FORCE

By Roan Novachez

I've got notecards to study for my speech, but I doubt I'll even need them, because I know the material so well.

And, then, um, once your mind is cleared — oh, you need to clear your mind, uh...

Um, so, clear your mind, and, like, meditate, and, um... keep doing it. Um...

Can't read this one...

Uh, thank you.

CLAP
CLAP

Oh, and I made these to hand out to everyone.

Thank you, Roan. We'll all have to meditate on your speech, I think!

Can I sit down yet?!

QUADDAY

Apparently the most successful part of my speech was my minicomic handout, which everyone liked. Except Cronah, of course. He said if other people helped me put the minicomics together, then it wasn't really a "solo presentation." I asked Pasha how he thought my speech went, and he said it was good but that I said "um" and "like" a lot. I got a "B" for my grade, so it wasn't a total disaster. Bill asked if I used the Force to focus while I was giving my speech, but I was too distracted by my notecards being all out of order.

Um, like, um, um, uh, like, like, um, uh, like

HOW I SOUNDED

I think the best speech was Gaiana's, about how to sense great disturbances in the environment by using the Force. She's great.

Feel the trees... now sense any animals in them. How are they feeling?

CLASS PET "VOORPEE" DELIGHTS AND TEACHES

This year at Jedi Academy, students have been enjoying taking turns to care for a voorpak, from the planet Naboo, which the Padawans have named "Voorpee." Gaiana, who organized the class pet program, says students will "study Voorpee's behavior and mannerisms, learning about diets and natural habitats." Voorpee is on loan from the Naboo Zoo.

EWOK PILOT   By Roan Novachez

THE PADAWAN OBSERVER Vol. MXIII #4

holomail

FROM: master_yoda_642
TO: Padawan Class Group
SUBJECT: Important Field Trip
Information

OPTIONS
◀ REPLY
▶ FORWARD
▢ PRINT
◯ POST TO HOLOBOOK

WHEN: WEEK SEVEN
WHERE: THE PLANET HOTH
PURPOSE: To study animals surviving on the frozen planet in order to learn how to adapt to extreme conditions.

ACTIVITIES: Camp in the ice caves below the surface, observe herds of tauntauns, and search for any vegetation.

NOTES: As always, students will be accompanied by Jedi chaperones, who will most likely be more than capable of handling problems such as ice scrabblers, wampas, pirates, smugglers, and ice worms.

CHAPERONES: Master Yoda, Mr. Garfield, T-P30, AND RW-22.

ITEMS TO BRING: Extra clothes, waterproof boots, snowshoes, long underwear, gloves, sunglasses, ice cube trays, scarf, hat, Hoth chocolate mix.

DUODAY

The field trip to Hoth was a lot of fun, although at first it looked like it was going to be super-boring...

THIS IS HOW THE PLANET HOTH LOOKS <u>EVERYWHERE</u>

Growing up on a desert planet, I had no idea how cold it would be. Fortunately, I brought extra-super-thick socks. Unfortunately, my boots wouldn't fit over them. Pasha let me borrow some of his extra socks.

Our first activity was to look for any vegetation. Gaiana teamed up with Bill and Tegan before I could join their group. I went with Pasha, and he showed Egon and me how to follow the tauntaun trails to find where the herds have foraged for lichen. We also learned that tauntauns do get some moisture from the lichen,

Yoda on Hoth

but they also have specially adapted tongues to lick the ice walls of their caves without getting their tongues stuck... Greer wasn't so lucky!

Do you have your lightsaber, Mr. Garfield?

The first night, Silva turned the heat on too high, so we had to spend part of the morning drying off our clothes. Then Ronald went out before his clothes had completely

dried and got frozen. We debated leaving him there while we all went sledding, but took him back inside

My arms won't bend!

the ice base to thaw out first. Sledding was AWESOME. There are huge hills and some of them had jumps. Even Cyrus and Cronah were impressed by my big jump.

The bad part was having to carry the sled back up the hill...

That was epic, Roan.

I want to do that.

What was your favorite part of our Hoth field trip?
POSTED BY ADMIN.

The Wampa attack was AWESOME, obviously.

Sledding! I've never gone sledding before.

I'd never seen SNOW before, that was pretty great. And sledding.

I like tauntauns - I wish I wasn't allergic and could've rode one!

Don't you mean you wish you weren't scared of them?

The tauntauns are so stinky, no wonder Bill likes them.

It was so cold, you can't really smell them, it wasn't so stinky.

You couldn't smell them because of how bad YOU stink, Roan.

I'm surprised the tauntaun let you ride it, Cronah.

My favorite part was seeing how goofy Shi-Fara looked on a tauntaun.

The only thing goofier would be a tauntaun riding a tauntaun!

63

HEXADAY

Every time I post on Holobook, it seems like Cronah and Cyrus have to say something mean to me. I know they don't like me that much, but they're never that rude when they talk to me in class or wherever. They're jerks to pretty much everyone on Holobook, but if you say anything, they notice you and write even MORE mean stuff. I'm supposed to be getting homework done, anyway. I've been studying for the star pilot simulator a lot, because I want to get the high score in class. So far, Gaiana and Pasha got high scores, which is okay, but one week Cronah got it, and I can't let that happen again!

Let me know if you need any tips, Roan!

Pilot of the Month

Moktok nub powa!

Ikee nyeta go cona!

Do you think Ewok Pilot and Jawa Pilot are a little too competitive?

I've finally gotten the hang of the star pilot simulators. I would've done better from the ~~beggining~~ beginning if we had REAL starships to fly. It's hard to feel the Force as a Jedi pilot when everything you're seeing in the cockpit is a holocomputer-generated image. The graphics on the video screen don't even look real! Egon has

A trail of ants?

Starship? Or shoe?

planet? Asteroid? One-eyed smiley-face?

video games that are more realistic. Mr. Garfield still hates me, too. I got the high score yesterday, and he made

You should've altered course by .02 degrees at this point...

Hrm.

Hmph.

his usual grumpy face and gave me a lecture, pointing out all the things I could've done better or differently.

And then Gaiana seemed annoyed that I did better than her. When She did better than me, I told her "good job" and everything.

ATTENTION PADAWANS

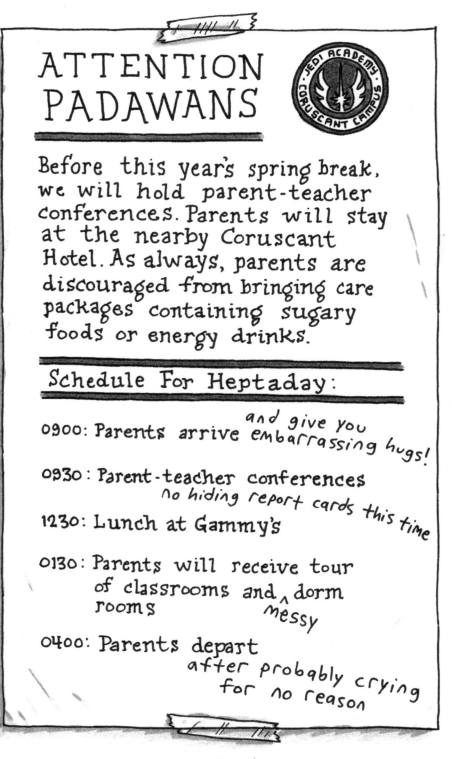

Before this year's spring break, we will hold parent-teacher conferences. Parents will stay at the nearby Coruscant Hotel. As always, parents are discouraged from bringing care packages containing sugary foods or energy drinks.

Schedule For Heptaday:

0900: Parents arrive *and give you embarrassing hugs!*

0930: Parent-teacher conferences *no hiding report cards this time*

1230: Lunch at Gammy's

0130: Parents will receive tour of classrooms and *messy* dorm rooms

0400: Parents depart *after probably crying for no reason*

HEXADAY

I'm pretty excited for parent-teacher conferences tomorrow. I'll finally get to see my grades, and I know they'll be way better than my first semester at Jedi Academy. I may even be getting all "A's". Since Dad is coming, I'll get to show him how well I'm doing in star pilot flight training. It'll also be fun to show Ollie around. He gets so happy when I use the Force, he'll have his mind blown by everyone at Jedi Academy! I'm glad that Ollie's coming, because maybe Mom will be too busy taking care of him to embarrass me too much.

STUDENT: ROAN NOVACHEZ		
LEVEL: PADAWAN	SEMESTER: THREE	
HOMEROOM: MASTER YODA		

REPORT CARD

CLASS	NOTES	GRADE
ADVANCED USING THE FORCE (MASTER YODA)	Roan's size mattered not, this semester.	A-
HISTORY OF THE JEDI ORDER (MRS. PILTON)	Excellent, except for study of major events during the Force Wars.	B+
GALACTIC ECOLOGY (PRINCIPAL MAR)	VERY GOOD UNDERSTAND-ING OF INTERPLANETARY ECOSYSTEMS.	A
HYPERALGEBRA (MRS. PILTON)	Roan is very close to knowing all the basic hyperspace equations.	a
STAR PILOT FLIGHT TRAINING, PT. 1. (MR. GARFIELD)	AFTER A ROUGH START, ROAN IMPROVED, BUT IS NOT ACHIEVING FULL POTENTIAL.	C+
PUBLIC SPEAKING (LIBRARIAN LACKBAR)	Roan needs more practice and confidence.	B-
PHYSICAL EDUCATION (KITMUM)		😮

Parent-teacher conferences weren't a TOTAL disaster, at least. Of course, Mr. Garfield had to figure out a way to give me a bad grade and said I only deserved a "C+." I thought Dad would be disappointed with me (again), but he wasn't, he just gave me some helpful advice. Everyone really liked Ollie. They thought he was adorable, especially the girls.

> Just stay focused, and don't give up!

Mom and Dad got to meet Gaiana finally, and Mom pinched me for some reason. I thought Gaiana might eat lunch with us, since her parents weren't even there, but she seemed like she was in a hurry. After lunch I found out Gaiana went

> Burp!
> escuse me!
> He's so cute!

home early for spring break, I wonder why she didn't say good-bye. I also got to meet Pasha's parents. They're super-nice! They invited me to come visit for spring break, and Mom and Dad said that I could. So I won't even have to spend spring break doing a bunch of chores at home. Too bad for Dav, ha! This will be the first time I've taken an actual trip for spring break, which is the opposite of Pasha — he usually goes somewhere instead of staying home. Pasha's dad says he'll show us some of the different things he studies at the museum where he works. The WEIRDEST part about the day was Cronah and Cyrus. They were actually... *nice* to me. Maybe now they can see how well I use the Force, AND that I'm a better pilot? They were there when I was saying good-bye to my family and they even shook my dad's hand. I thought they were going to play some kind of joke, but they didn't. They didn't even laugh when Mom totally embarrassed me before she got on the shuttle for home!

DIRECTIONS TO PASHA'S HOUSE

1. Leave Coruscant by taking the Perlemian Trade Route AWAY from the Galactic Core

2. Transfer to the Hydian Way heading a bunch of parsecs toward the planet Corsin

3. Turn right

4. End at 120 Obroa-Skai

Pasha's House

Hutt Space

Coruscant

Galactic Core

Weewa!

Hoth (Brrrrn)

Endor (Ewok Pilot's house)

Tatooine (Roan's house)

Mustafar

If you end up in Hutt space you went the wrong way

HEPTADAY

Today I was supposed to go with Pasha and his dad to visit the Museum of Applied Photonics, but there was some

NO.

MEAN!

kind of problem and the security guard wouldn't let me in. I could only stay in the food court. Pasha offered to stay with me, but I told him he should go ahead, so Pasha went with his dad. I expected Pasha to insist on staying! Pasha's dad just needed to pick some things up, so I figured it wouldn't take too long, but then it ended up being, like, three hours. Tomorrow, we're planning on going to the Obroan Institute for ~~Archeology~~ Archaeology, where Pasha's dad works. I probably won't be allowed to go inside there, either, so I'm going to bring my sketchbook with me for sure.

probably what I'll be stuck doing tomorrow, too

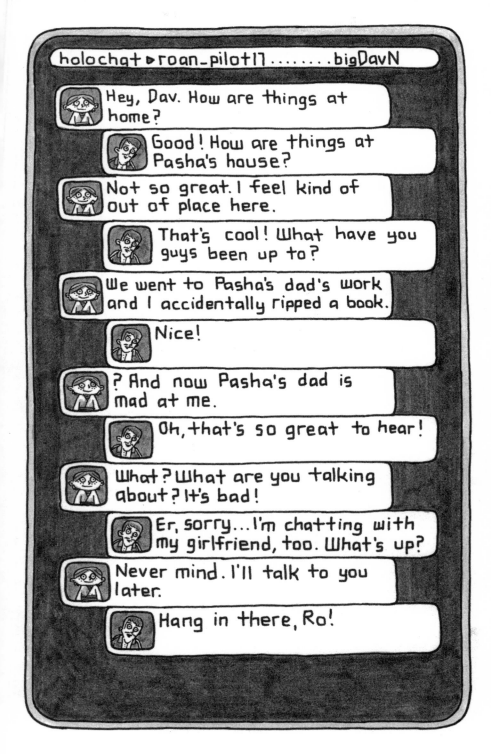

Today I met some
of Pasha's friends.
They all had some
kind of secret
handshake, but
Pasha said he'd
have to teach it to

me later, because it's pretty ~~complacated~~
complicated. Then they were talking about
Jedi Academy, and I was confused, because
I didn't know any of the teachers they were
mentioning. I said something about the
Archives, and they looked at me like I was
a weirdo. Then Pasha laughed, because he
realized I didn't know there's a different
Jedi Academy on Obroa-Skai that's for Jedi
Research Specialties. That's where all of
his friends go. So basically I made a
fool of myself. Then Pasha's friends invited
him to hang out all afternoon, so I
had to sit there the whole time
feeling like an idiot. Especially when
they started talking about their
favorite holotelevision show. I don't
even know what it's called because
you can't see it on Tatooine.

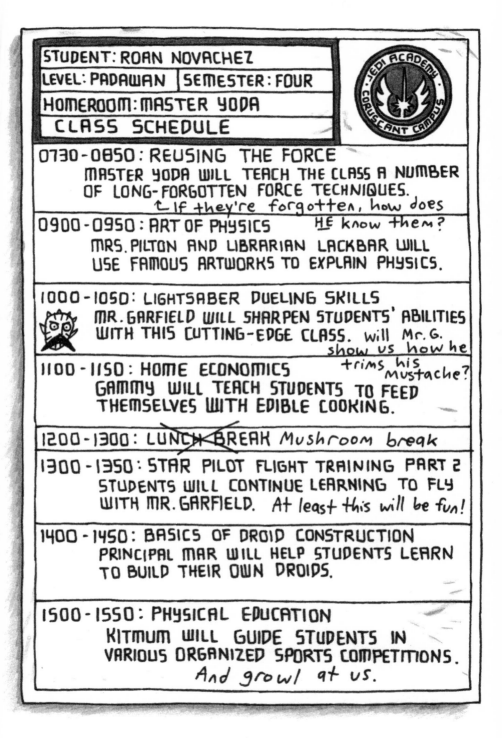

STUDENT: ROAN NOVACHEZ

LEVEL: PADAWAN | SEMESTER: FOUR

HOMEROOM: MASTER YODA

CLASS SCHEDULE

0730-0850: REUSING THE FORCE
MASTER YODA WILL TEACH THE CLASS A NUMBER OF LONG-FORGOTTEN FORCE TECHNIQUES.
↳ If they're forgotten, how does HE know them?

0900-0950: ART OF PHYSICS
MRS. PILTON AND LIBRARIAN LACKBAR WILL USE FAMOUS ARTWORKS TO EXPLAIN PHYSICS.

1000-1050: LIGHTSABER DUELING SKILLS
MR. GARFIELD WILL SHARPEN STUDENTS' ABILITIES WITH THIS CUTTING-EDGE CLASS. Will Mr. G. show us how he trims his mustache?

1100-1150: HOME ECONOMICS
GAMMY WILL TEACH STUDENTS TO FEED THEMSELVES WITH EDIBLE COOKING.

1200-1300: ~~LUNCH BREAK~~ Mushroom break

1300-1350: STAR PILOT FLIGHT TRAINING PART 2
STUDENTS WILL CONTINUE LEARNING TO FLY WITH MR. GARFIELD. At least this will be fun!

1400-1450: BASICS OF DROID CONSTRUCTION
PRINCIPAL MAR WILL HELP STUDENTS LEARN TO BUILD THEIR OWN DROIDS.

1500-1550: PHYSICAL EDUCATION
KITMUM WILL GUIDE STUDENTS IN VARIOUS ORGANIZED SPORTS COMPETITIONS. And growl at us.

NEW STAR PILOT SIMULATORS ARRIVE AT JEDI ACADEMY

Just in time for the new semester, Jedi Academy has received new and improved star pilot simulators, with advanced technology

that will give students a more realistic flying experience. Mr.

OLD   NEW

Garfield stated the old simulators were "just fine" and the only reason for new ones was "politics."

EWOK PILOT   By Roan Novachez

Ewok Pilot, what are you doing to your ship? Ji?

kush drojh?!

You should ask Jawa Pilot to help you fix it. He has lots of parts.

Tyeht danti? Yanna kuzu peekay?

STAR PILOT FLIGHT TRAINING NOTES

Avoiding Obstacles

- If you need to go faster, divert power from shields to increase power to engines. More dangerous to crash without shields, so DO NOT CRASH.

- Before avoiding obstacles by turning, make sure there isn't another obstacle where you're turning to.

- Pay attention to onboard navigation computer. Typos are #1 cause of star pilots going the wrong direction.

- Check mirrors to make sure you're pointed AWAY from planets when entering hyperspace.

- Space is really dark so keep your lights on and make sure your starship has the proper reflective markings.

My life is turning into a giant FAIL. After class I saw Pasha and Gaiana talking in the hallway, and Pasha was holding her hand! Maybe HE likes Gaiana now and that's why he's being weird to me since spring break. What a jerk. I'm not talking to either of them until they explain. Mr. Garfield still HATES me. Even Cyrus and Cronah think Mr. Garfield has it in for me. He always finds an excuse to mark my grade down. So even though I'm doing everything perfect, my grade will end up WORSE than last semester. The only good thing in my life is that we finally got to use the new star pilot simulators this week. They're so much better than the old ones — they even move around so it feels like you're actually flying. It's good that we have helmets to wear. With my luck, I'll probably break the new simulators, too.

What'd you do, eat his lunch?

No.

← Dizzy from loop-the-loops

THINGS GAMMY SAYS

NUG UR TOG THOGK!

* Make sure you chew your food well. Especially if it's chewy.

HURG NG STUR!

* Gently spread the frosting on top of the cake and sprinkle with insect eggs.

GRN GRK TOK!

* For added taste, top with fruit.

EGRN DREG GROFKT!!

* Maybe a moldy cherry cut into starburst shape.

GRUNT!

* Don't worry about messing up a recipe, the food will still be edible. You won't starve, it'll just taste horrible.

CLASS ASSIGNMENT

Students will work in groups of five to build their own fully operational droids. You will be expected to work together, sharing responsibility equally. Students in each group will all receive the same grade.

- Droids are not required to communicate, but extra credit will be given to droids with multiple functions.
- Droids must have at least one primary specialized function (e.g. sweeping and vacuuming floors).
- NO WEAPONS. Any droid equipped with lasers will result in a failing grade.
- Droids will be judged on these criteria: function, design, reliability, originality, and the vague, undefinable sense of whether the droid has "it."

QUADDAY

Supposedly, the groups for our droid construction project were picked ~~randomly~~ randomly by a holocomputer, but I think the holocomputer is playing a joke on me. Not only is Cronah in my group, but none of my real friends are....

Cyrus is in my group, he's at least been cooler to me lately. I think it's partly because he met my dad, who's a real starfighter pilot and kind of a big deal. Now I'm going to have to choose between following along with what everyone else wants to do on the project, or trying to get them to listen to me, which will be impossible. This project's destiny is TOTAL DISASTER.

what our droid will end up looking like

NOTES

To tell if egg is ready to eat, crack open. If creature hatches and attacks you, egg should have been cooked longer.

*Add mushrooms to your cupcakes so it feels like you're eating something healthy. (May taste different?!)

IMPORTANT!

-Lightsaber should not be used to cut butter (it tends to melt all the butter) or bread (will toast the entire loaf).

-Lightsaber CAN be used to carve turkey for dinner. Make sure to thoroughly wash lightsaber afterward.

97

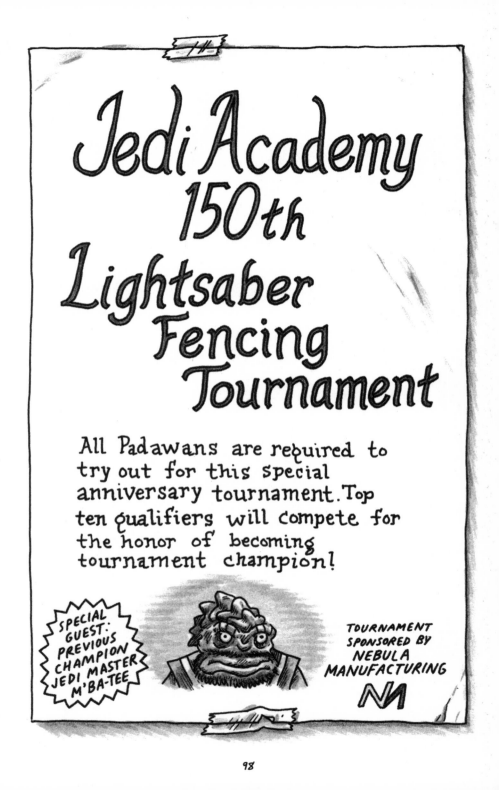

Jedi Academy
150th
Lightsaber
Fencing
Tournament

All Padawans are required to try out for this special anniversary tournament. Top ten qualifiers will compete for the honor of becoming tournament champion!

SPECIAL GUEST: PREVIOUS CHAMPION JEDI MASTER M'BA-TEE

TOURNAMENT SPONSORED BY NEBULA MANUFACTURING

TRIDAY

I'm going to start training more at
lightsaber fencing. If I practice enough
in secret, everyone will be surprised when
I do well at the tournament. Maybe I can
even win the whole thing? I've been trying
to find someone to train with, but I'm
still not talking to Pasha so he's out.
But now I figured out a way to practice
<u>while</u> my group is making the droid —
we're going to build a training droid
for lightsaber fencing. It's actually
been okay working with Cyrus and
Cronah. They're kind of letting me be
the "idea guy." So I won't have to do as
much of the ~~tedios~~ tedious work of
putting the droid together.

LIGHTSABER FENCING TRAINING DROID

Multiple optical sensors

Vocal intimidator (will trash-talk you)

Shutdown target

← parrot perch

360° locomotion system

Adjustable Height

bubble gum dispenser

Bells and whistles

Possible Additional Functions:
- Heavy Metal Drummer
- Flag waver
- Can wash starships?
  Cafeteria dishwasher?
- Practice Soccer goalie

Multiple swivel arms with Kung fu battle grip

PENTADAY

Lately, every time I try to hang out with Bill or Egon it seems like they're busy. Actually, we _DID_ have plans to hang out yesterday, but after waiting an hour I gave up. Bill made it sound like it was just a mistake, but it wouldn't surprise me if Pasha is trying to turn them against me, too. I've hardly talked to Gaiana this semester and

I was waiting by the math room.

Oh. We were at the biology lab.

Sorry.

I bet she's just hanging out with Pasha, and he's probably telling her how awful I am. I was going to ask Tegan what she thought Gaiana was thinking, but Tegan would just tell me to talk to Gaiana, which I tried. It was a big disaster. At least I'll get better grades this semester, since all I do is study, and not hang out with my friends.

Hi, Gaiana, how are you?

Okay.

THE LONGEST CONVERSATION I HAD WITH GAIANA LAST MONTH

I have been hanging out with Cyrus and Cronah a little, mostly because we've been working on our group droid project. The droid is looking good! They let me basically design the whole thing. At the start of this year I never would've imagined working on something with them, let alone me leading

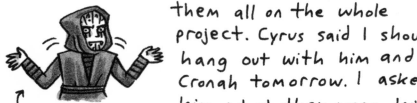

them all on the whole project. Cyrus said I should hang out with him and Cronah tomorrow. I asked

I wish I could shrug like that

him what they were doing and he just shrugged. It's cool— they don't even need to have a plan of what they're going to do. Cyrus and I also had a really long conversation, about Corellian starfighter ~~mano maneuvers~~ maneuvers.

I guess I just needed to get to know him and Cronah to realize they aren't ALWAYS total jerks. We're going to practice lightsaber fencing... I'll bet I can learn some new techniques from them.

I'm not sure we can use this method, Ewok Pilot.

Dangar!

ART OF PHYSICS
IMPORTANT EXAMPLES

Lackbar/Pilton

The Hyperspace Night

Painting shows how perception of astronomical objects changes when a starship enters hyperspace

The Great Wave Off Naboo

Shows behavior of water molecules when a sando aqua mo~~nster~~ approache~~s~~

ROAN -
LET'S SKIP MR. G.'S CLASS.
CRONAH AND I HAVE SOMETHING TO SHOW YOU.
—CY

Monoday Afternoon On Yavin 4

~~...~~t style of drawing ~~o~~ptical illusion using ~~an~~d distance

~~...~~ Rhythm

~~vis~~ual chaos could represent interactions of atomic particles affected by the Force

TRIDAY

Tomorrow we present our group droid construction projects. I'm going to look over ours one last time tonight. It turned out well! We'll even be able to use it to train for the lightsaber fencing tournament. Since everyone else in my group usually wears dark robes, we thought I should wear a dark robe for the presentation, so we all look the same. Cyrus had some old robes that didn't fit him anymore,

Hood = Awesome!

and he said I could just keep them. I think I look pretty cool in them, actually. I mean, they're a little big, but everyone wears robes that are a little big. That was nice of Cyrus, and then Cronah suggested that I get to name the droid, since it was my design. I decided we should call it the Multi-Armed Dueling Simulator droid. So we call him M.A.D.S.

I WILL DESTROY YOU!

I WILL DEFEAT YOU!

MADS

That was a most interesting cafeteria droid we just saw...

Cyrus, Jo-Ahn, Roan, Cronah, and Greer...would you like to present your droid?

Thank you, Principal Mar. As you can see, this Multi-Armed Duel Simulator droid — or "M.A.D.S." — is designed for training and preparation in lightsaber dueling.

It's full of specialized design functions.

Each arm is covered with lightsaber-resistant foam padding.

The multiple optical sensors can detect a full 360° of movement.

By combining a swivel torso and wheeled feet, the droid is super mobile.

And the center target tracks points earned in fencing.

HEPTADAY

Our droid got the best grade in class Principal Mar seemed impressed by how much work we put into it. Of course, I think the other droids weren't that great. Pasha and Bill made a "Class Schedule Assistant" droid that basically leads you to your next class. I think you'd only need it the first day of class and after that it'd just trip you. I've been having a lot of fun hanging out with Cyrus and Cronah. They're pretty cool — they even have some

video games I'd never seen. Way cooler than the games Egon is usually showing us. If Pasha played them he'd probably make a big deal about them being too violent. He's probably jealous of my group, because he had to do extra work with his group since their droid malfunctioned. Cyrus says that the only people who think school grades are a competition are the people who aren't doing as well.

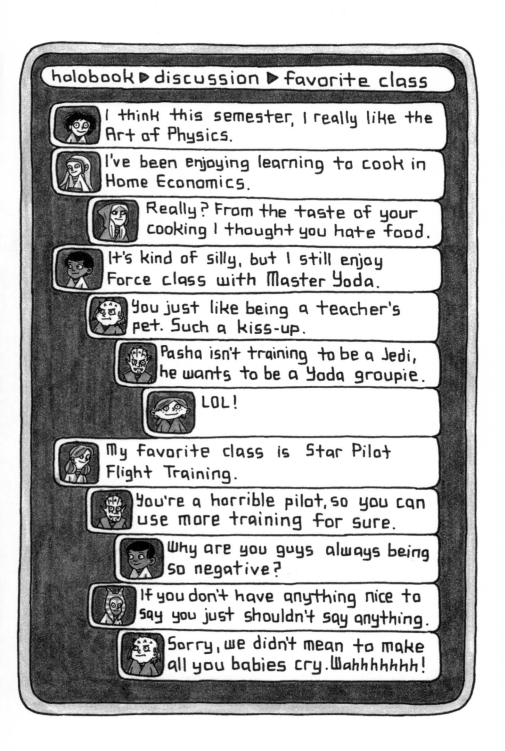

I think this semester, I really like the Art of Physics.

I've been enjoying learning to cook in Home Economics.

Really? From the taste of your cooking I thought you hate food.

It's kind of silly, but I still enjoy Force class with Master Yoda.

You just like being a teacher's pet. Such a kiss-up.

Pasha isn't training to be a Jedi, he wants to be a Yoda groupie.

LOL!

My favorite class is Star Pilot Flight Training.

You're a horrible pilot, so you can use more training for sure.

Why are you guys always being so negative?

If you don't have anything nice to say you just shouldn't say anything.

Sorry, we didn't mean to make all you babies cry. Wahhhhhhhh!

The Padawan Observer

EDITED BY THE STUDENTS OF JEDI ACADEMY · VOL.MXIII #8

MASTER YODA SHUTS DOWN HOLOBOOK DUE TO COMMENTS

In an unexpected move, Holobook has been completely shut down by Master Yoda, due to the large number of mean and insulting comments appearing recently. "Behave like this, Padawans should not. Off, Holobook will be, until better manners, the Padawans have." Master Yoda warned that although writing mean comments may flow easily for some, they can lead to the dark side. Students may still use Holomail.

INSIDE:

MISSING!

"Voorpee", the class pet voorpak, has gone missing!

- Does not actually answer to "Voorpee" but may come if you make cute noises.
- May look like a piece of dirt or lint, so be careful to not sweep up.
- Please help find Voorpee!
- Also, watch your step.

HEXADAY

Voorpee is lost, but it's not my fault.
Some of the other students think it is
anyway. I heard that Pasha told Gaiana
he thought that someone said I made a
joke about losing Voorpee or something.
Just because I was with Cronah and Cyrus
when they took Voorpee out of his cage
doesn't mean I'm the one who lost him.
I know Gaiana didn't take him, but why
didn't anyone think it was her, since
SHE likes Voorpee so much? Plus, she's
been acting weird all semester,
especially to me. Whatever, I don't
care. I used to, but not anymore. Not
really. I think.

The other thing that happened is that Master Yoda shut off access to Holobook because people were being too mean. Maybe it got a little out of hand, but I think some people just don't know how to take a joke. Pasha has been mean to me, too, not on Holobook but in REAL LIFE. He still hasn't said anything to me about Gaiana, and when he found out I

You shouldn't do that, Roan.

Mr. Bossypants know-it-all

pretended to be sick to get out of some homework he started lecturing me. It kind of hurts that he didn't even realize that's the first time he talked to me in, like, a month! I just ignored him. The only problem with ignoring Pasha is that our Marksman-H Combat Remote is missing, and I can't ask him where it is. He must be hiding it from me on purpose. Unless Voorpee took it. (NOT likely.)

Bew!

Bew! Bew!

THINGS YODA SAID THIS WEEK

LIGHTSABER DUELING SKILLS
TAKE-HOME QUIZ

(B)

STUDENT: _Roan Novachez_
INSTRUCTOR: _Mr. Garfield_

1. Fill in the missing movement for basic lightsaber forms.

A SIMPLE STICK FIGURE WOULD BE ENOUGH HERE, ROAN!

2. What three moves should be used together in Form Ⅴ?

   rapid spin, somersault, cartwheel

~~3.~~ What is the first Form to use in a real-life lightsaber duel?

   Form Ⅱ - Makashi Form

NO- FORM ZERO: FIND A NONVIOLENT SOLUTION

DUODAY

I've been getting a lot more training for the lightsaber fencing tournament, thanks to M.A.D.S., Cyrus, and Cronah. The other day they told Ronald he could come with us, which annoyed me. They seem to like him, but he's always cheating and just seems slimy to me. Cronah says Ronald actually has some good ideas for ~~stratagy~~ strategy but I don't want to have to listen to Ronald just to win in lightsaber fencing.

Fortunately, the height adjustment got stuck on M.A.D.S. so we spent the whole time fixing that and didn't have to practice with Ronald.

Unfortunately, I couldn't get the storage space (where we've been keeping M.A.D.S.)

unlocked. So I ended up keeping M.A.D.S. in my room last night, which made it hard to sleep, because I swear he was staring at me all night!

Yoda is making me go on a totally boring field trip to watch the Galactic Senate as part of my punishment for the food fight. He said something like "learn peaceful solutions, you must." The teachers think I started it. Even though Cyrus and Cronah told them what happened, I guess, NO ONE believed me when I said Pasha was the one who really started it. I thought at first maybe Pasha was lying, and I was getting angrier, because Master Yoda and Principal Mar wouldn't listen to me.

But Master Yoda said they knew what happened and that was the end of it. Master Yoda gave me this look like he was REALLY disappointed in me and I felt really stupid. Even seeing the food in Ronald's hair after the food fight didn't cheer me up, and the more I think about it, the more I wish I hadn't thrown any food. At least my dodgeball skills came in handy.

GALACTIC SENATE NOTES

didn't see any Ewoks?

- Senators represent inhabited planets from across galaxy, like to talk
- Senate responsible for regulating trade, maintaining galactic maps, try to solve intergalactic problems without causing more intergalactic problems
- Led by Supreme Chancellor and Vice Chair. "Vice Chair" is not actually a chair but position of authority
- Senator Blagotine introduced bill to change how bills are introduced by Senators (not that kind of Bill)

Good to meet you.

MY LIFE NOTES

- How did I not know Gaiana's dad was sick?
- Pasha is dating Shi-Fara?!
- I am such a moron!

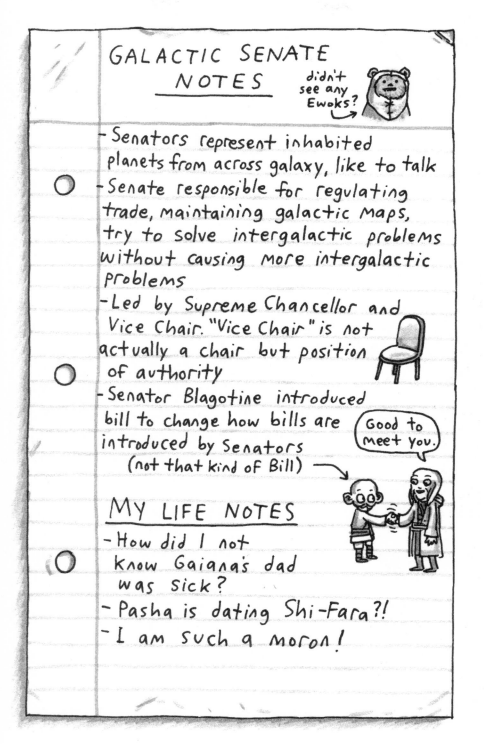

HEPTADAY

So, I'm an idiot. And a jerk. I mean, I'm totally NOT an idiot or a jerk, but I guess I have kind of acted like one lately. The whole semester I've been thinking Gaiana was acting weird about me when really her dad was sick. But now she doesn't really want to talk to me. I don't think Pasha does, either. I thought he was trying to date Gaiana, but he was just helping her, which is what I should've been doing. When Shi-Fara told me what Pasha was really doing, I almost puked like Bill. Now I need to figure out how to fix things, but I can't really talk to anyone. The only people still talking to me are Cyrus and Cronah, but I feel like they don't really care. They would

Tell us more about your "feelings," Roan.

Let us get you some tissues.

probably just laugh if I told them what I was thinking about. Especially since they can't give anyone a hard time on Holobook right now. Maybe if I can talk to Pasha, he can explain stuff to Gaiana. Maybe I'll get on the same lightsaber fencing tournament team as Gaiana and Pasha, and then I'll have an excuse to talk to them. That would be too easy. It's like the Senators— they have a reason to talk, and all they do is argue. It was ~~frustrating~~ frustrating to watch them. Afterward, I was talking to Master Yoda, and he made it sound like I was actually complaining about myself, and not the Senators...

holomail

FROM: master_yoda_642
TO: Padawan Class Group
SUBJECT: 150th Lightsaber
Fencing Tournament

OPTIONS
◀ REPLY
▶ FORWARD
⬛ PRINT
⬤ POST TO HOLOBOOK

Dear Padawan Class,
The 150th Annual Lightsaber Fencing
Tournament, this year is. Chosen by our
special guest, Jedi Master M'Ba-Tee,
the matches were, hmm?

Jo-Ahn
VS
Gaiana

Ronald
VS
Silva

Cronah
VS
Tegan

Cyrus
VS
Egon

Roan
VS
Pasha

Good luck, heh heh heh!
　　　　　　　　-Master Yoda

135

The lightsaber fencing tournament is tomorrow, and it's turning into a disaster already. First of all, I'm matched up against Pasha. How am I supposed to make up with Pasha when I have to fight him? And to make things worse, Cronah and Cyrus are trying to make me cheat.

The odds of Cronah winning are

What are the odds of you getting broken?

I told them I wouldn't but now they're threatening to tell Master Yoda that I took Voorpee, when I know it was Cronah who did something. I can't say anything now, because it'll look like I was part of it anyway and I'll still get in trouble. All Cronah and Cyrus care about is winning. I don't know why I cared so much about what they think of me. If I tell on them now, I'll have zero friends. Maybe I deserve no friends, since I've been such a bad friend. All I've done lately is mess things up, but at least I can TRY to stop messing things up.

NEBULA MANUFACTURING PRESENTS

150th ANNUAL CORUSCANT JEDI ACADEMY LIGHTSABER FENCING TOURNAMENT

The Coruscant Jedi Academy Lightsaber Fencing Tournament began when Jedi Master Jan Mincénte would challenge each of his Padawan students to lightsaber fencing duels. He quickly grew tired of winning easily, and decided it made more sense for students to test their skills against one another. Since the first tournament, many of our most well-known Jedi Knights have competed in, and won, the tournament. This includes Jedi Master M'Ba-Tee, whose skills made him the champion of the 12th Annual Tournament.

142

MONODAY

I was really proud of Pasha winning the tournament, but I'm also proud of myself. I mean, I think I did well, even though I lost, but I didn't cheat. Best of all, I managed to make up with Pasha. We were feeling so good after the tournament that Pasha didn't even mind they spelled his name wrong on his trophy. Then Pasha invited me to come with his team for their victory dinner. Gaiana was sitting across the table from me, and since I was

feeling so good, I thought I'd try to talk to her. She just gave me a kind of angry look and said she didn't really want to talk to me. So I still need to find a way to apologize to her.

Have you seen Ewok Pilot? Now he's missing, too?!

Meanwhile...

Tyeht danti?

Ookwass dok pundwa keena?

Yub yub.

Hey Ro,

I think I want to give you this advice on paper, so you can tape it into your journal <u>forever</u>. Take it from your incredibly wise, emotionally intelligent brother... if you really want to talk to Gaiana, just make sure <u>you're</u> listening to <u>her</u>. Otherwise, you might as well just be talking to yourself. Good luck!

　　　　　　　　　－Dav

P.S. When you take your final star pilot exam, remember rule number one:
　　　DON'T PANIC!

TRIDAY

Master Yoda decided I would have to write an apology to the Naboo Zoo for what happened with Voorpee. I think he may think there was someone else involved. Maybe I just should've told Master Yoda about Cronah and Cyrus anyway, since they both think I told on them, even though I didn't. They were already mad at me about not cheating to help them win the lightsaber tournament, and now they're super mad at me. But I didn't want to be a snitch. The important thing is that Voorpee is okay. Gaiana is also super mad at me. She won't even talk to

You're gonna pay for this, Roan!

Big time!

me. Even if I told her the whole truth, I don't think she'd believe me anyway. I haven't gotten much sleep, because I'm trying to think of a way I can make her understand. Now I need to get back to studying for the star pilot flight training exam. If I don't pass that, I might as well quit Jedi Academy....

Methods for avoiding asteroids

- Controlled spin (dip wings)
- stay <u>CLOSE</u> to asteroids
- Don't move away too fast or you risk running into other asteroids
- study asteroid movement patterns

- use asterods for cove

Stayed up too late and fell asleep studying

Drool stain →

STAR PILOT FLIGHT TRAINING
FINAL EXAM

This test requires each student to complete a flight path through an asteroid belt from Planet "A" to Planet "B." Grades will be determined by distance, duration, and damage.

While grades are assessed individually, it is expected you will work together to remove obstacles, cover one another, and warn of potential dangers. Students will be able to track one another's progress, and should maintain awareness of their Health/Damage Meter status.

FLIGHT LEADER: _ROAN_
WINGMEN: _CYRUS_
CRONAH

153

PENTADAY

The way this year started, I wasn't sure
I was going to pass star pilot flight training.
By the time this semester was half over,
I wasn't sure I'd have any friends left. So
it felt good to help Gaiana (and Shi-Fara),
even though I didn't end up with that
good a score at the
end of the exam.
Mr. Garfield had a
hard time deciding
what grade to give
me. He likes to
give me bad grades.
Even though I crashed,
I figured he might actually give me
an "A" because of HOW I crashed. I was
even thinking maybe he doesn't WANT
to like me, but he does. He was
only going to give
me a "C-" until
Master Yoda talked
him into giving me
a "B-." Getting a
better grade than
Cyrus and Cronah
REALLY made them
mad, though.

Nice crash, Roan!

Way to blow it!

Thanks!

Interesting flying, that was, hm?

Hmph.

Not that I thought Cyrus and Cronah were going to be my friends after the flight exam, but I didn't think they would HATE me. Master Yoda put them on academic probation for next year's first semester because of what happened with Voorpee. Now they really think I snitched on them, but I didn't. The only person who I told what really happened was Pasha, and I made him promise to not tell ANYONE. Master Yoda is really smart, so maybe he used the Force to figure it out? Or he can talk to animals and

Cyrus? Cronah? Question them, we will...

Voorpee told him what happened? Maybe Cyrus and Cronah told on each other.

Ewok Pilot! You found Jawa Pilot!

But...

...what did you guys do to your starfighter?!

Opakwa!

Jeerota!

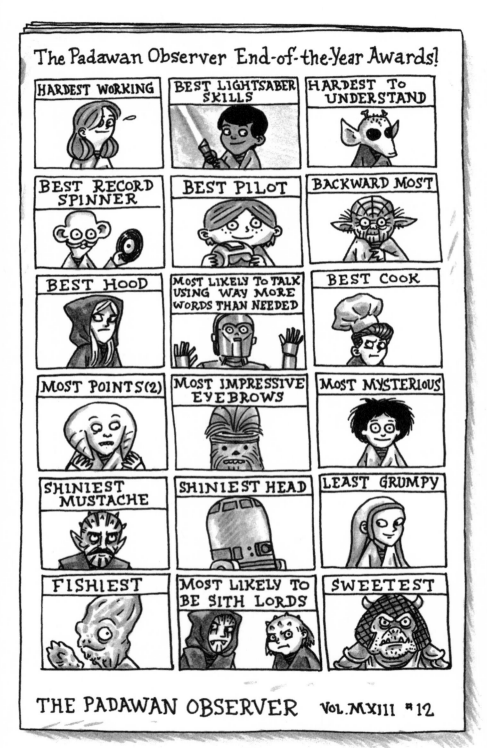

The Padawan Observer End-of-the-Year Awards!

HARDEST WORKING

BEST LIGHTSABER SKILLS

HARDEST TO UNDERSTAND

BEST RECORD SPINNER

BEST PILOT

BACKWARD MOST

BEST HOOD

MOST LIKELY TO TALK USING WAY MORE WORDS THAN NEEDED

BEST COOK

MOST POINTS (2)

MOST IMPRESSIVE EYEBROWS

MOST MYSTERIOUS

SHINIEST MUSTACHE

SHINIEST HEAD

LEAST GRUMPY

FISHIEST

MOST LIKELY TO BE SITH LORDS

SWEETEST

THE PADAWAN OBSERVER VOL. MXIII #12

CLASS	NOTES	GRADE
REUSING THE FORCE [MASTER YODA]	Use the Force outside of class more, Roan should, hm?	A
ART OF PHYSICS [MRS. PILTON/ LIBRARIAN LACKBAR]	Roan's thoughts were an excellent addition to this class	a-
LIGHTSABER DUELING SKILLS [MR. GARFIELD]	ROAN'S SKILLS IMPROVED, BUT HE NEEDS MORE FOCUS	A-
HOME ECONOMICS [GAMMY]		
STAR PILOT FLIGHT TRAINING, PT. 2 [MR. GARFIELD]	ROAN HASN'T REACHED HIS FULL POTENTIAL, MUST WORK HARDER	B-
BASICS OF DROID CONSTRUCTION [PRINCIPAL MAR]	ROAN COULD BE MORE ASSERTIVE WITH VOCAL DROID COMMANDS.	A
PHYSICAL EDUCATION [KITMUM]		

STUDENT: ROAN NOVACHEZ
LEVEL: PADAWAN   SEMESTER: FOUR
HOMEROOM: MASTER YODA
REPORT CARD

JEDI ACADEMY · CORUSCANT CAMPUS

DUODAY

I learned a lot this year, but not the way I expected to. Like, being in pilot training taught me about being a good friend. Or maybe learning to be a good friend made me a better pilot? Something like that. Mr. Garfield never really got around to liking me this year.

You still have a lot to learn.

A LOT.

I mean, you just have a ton to learn still.

Even when I did good, he would list a bunch of things I did wrong. I thought maybe Mr. Garfield was finally going to start liking me, because I've become a really good pilot, but he just doesn't care. I also thought Cyrus and Cronah were starting to like me, too, but they ended up being jerks and tried to make me look stupid. I'm even okay that Pasha beat me in lightsaber fencing, now that things are back to normal with us.

Roan, did you see what someone wrote about you on Holobook?

No, was it written by "Cronah-is-trying-to-make-me-feel-bad-but-totally-failing"?

So even though I thought it was silly how kitmum always wants to tell us that winning isn't important, maybe she has the right idea. I don't know how these teachers all know so much, except Master Yoda. If I were six hundred years old, I'd know EVERYTHING, too. But then Yoda goes and says things like this. →

Many lessons to teach their masters, students have. Heh heh heh!

I wonder if Master Yoda ever messed things up with his friends? Last year, I was worried about having any friends here, but it ended up being easy. This year, I wasn't worried at all, and I almost ended up losing ALL of my friends. That's another thing, I learned—if you want to find something out, sometimes you just have to ask. That seems really obvious when I write it down now. Gaiana isn't still mad at me, at least, but I don't know if she likes me the same. Maybe I can ask her. Sometime.

So, um, well... uh... okay...

Okay what?

WRITE YOUR OWN STORIES!

Use your favorite characters, make up new ones, or have you and your friends be the heroes!

Decide where your story is happening — on Earth or in a galaxy far, far away?

Make your story as long or as short as you want.

Use words, pictures, or even photo collage to tell your story.

Choose a theme for your story — is it about finding something? Winning a competition? Escaping danger? Or just telling a funny joke?

Make sure your story has a beginning and an end.

Share your stories with your friends!

Jeffrey Brown is a cartoonist and author of the bestselling **DARTH VADER AND SON** and its sequel **VADER'S LITTLE PRINCESS,** in addition to the **STAR WARS: JEDI ACADEMY** series. He lives in Chicago with his wife and two sons. Although he has not completed his Jedi training, he is close to completing his collection of Star Wars movie trading cards.

P.O. Box 120 Deerfield IL 60015-0120 USA